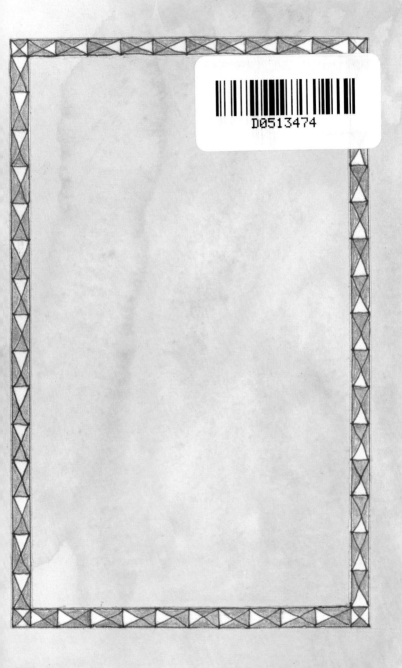

## NOTE TO PARENTS

This familiar Bible story has been retold in a sensitive and simple way so that young children can read and understand it for themselves. But the special message of the story remains unchanged. It is the message of God's love and care for us all.

# Joseph
# and his Coat of
# Many Colours

retold by Marjorie Newman
illustrated by Edgar Hodges

Copyright © MCMLXXXVIII by World International Publishing Limited.
All rights reserved.
Published in Great Britain by World International Publishing Limited.
An Egmont Company, Egmont House,
P.O. Box 111, Great Ducie Street,
Manchester M60 3BL.
Printed in Italy.
ISBN 7235 3006 8

Long ago, in the Bible lands, there lived
a boy called Joseph. He had a mother,
a father, ten big brothers and one small
brother. Joseph's ten big brothers didn't like
him, because he was their father Jacob's
favourite.

One day, Jacob gave Joseph a
gorgeous coat of many colours. Joseph's big
brothers were very jealous. They called him
names. And whenever they saw him, they
muttered, "It's not fair!" Joseph had to
pretend not to notice.

As Joseph grew older, he helped his brothers with the work. Sometimes he worked with the sheep. Sometimes he worked in the cornfield. But he always wore his coat of many colours.

One night, Joseph had a dream. He told it to his brothers. "I dreamed we were working in the cornfield. And your sheaves bowed down to my sheaf."

"What?" shouted his brothers. "Do you think we shall ever bow down to *you*?" And they hated him even more.

Joseph had another dream. "I dreamed the sun, the moon and eleven stars all bowed down to me!" he said.

Even Jacob wasn't pleased. "Do you think that your father, your mother, and your brothers will bow down to you?" he asked. But he didn't forget Joseph's dream . . .

Not long afterwards, Jacob said to Joseph,
"Your brothers have been away a long
time, looking after the sheep. Go and see if they
are all right. Then come back and tell me."
Gladly Joseph set off. This would be an
adventure!

Joseph expected to find his brothers at Shechem. But they weren't there! A man told him, "Your brothers have gone to Dothan, to find better grazing for the sheep."

"Oh," said Joseph. "Thank you."
He decided to walk on.

At Dothan, Joseph's brothers were sitting round a camp fire. Suddenly, they looked up. "Oh no!" they groaned. "Here comes the dreamer! This is our chance. Let's kill him!"

"Yes!" shouted all the brothers, except Reuben. "Throw his body into that hole! Tell everyone a wild animal has eaten him!"

"Wait!" cried Reuben. "We don't need to kill him! Let's just throw him into the hole and leave him! We'll still be rid of him!" Secretly, Reuben meant to come back and rescue Joseph. But his brothers didn't know that.

"Right!" they cried. And as soon as Joseph came near enough they grabbed him, tore off his coat, and threw him into the deep hole.

"Help!" cried Joseph. "I can't get out!" His brothers took no notice.

Joseph could hear his brothers laughing
and talking. He felt lonely and afraid.
He tried to remember that God loved him,
and would take care of him.

Reuben couldn't bear to sit with the others.
He went to see if the sheep were all right.
While he was gone, Judah cried, "Look!
There are some traders on camels! I've
got an idea!"

"Let's sell Joseph to those traders!" Judah said. "They'll take him to Egypt, and sell him in the slave market there! We shall be rid of him, *and* get some money!"

"Good idea!" laughed the others. Roughly, they pulled Joseph out of the hole. The traders paid twenty pieces of silver for him. And before Joseph quite knew what was happening, he found himself on the way to Egypt.

A little while later, Reuben came back.
He crept over to the hole to rescue Joseph.
But Joseph wasn't there. "He's gone!
Where is he?" Reuben shouted.

"We sold him as a slave," his brothers
answered.

Reuben was very upset.

The others killed a young goat, and dipped Joseph's coat in its blood. They took the coat back to their father and showed it to him. "My son has been torn to pieces by a wild animal!" wept Jacob. And no one could comfort him.

But Joseph was not dead. God was still taking care of him. Joseph had been sold to Potiphar, a captain of the guard at Pharaoh's palace. (Pharaoh was the ruler of all Egypt.) Joseph worked hard, and Potiphar was pleased. He put Joseph in charge of all his household.

But Potiphar's wife tried to make Joseph do
wrong. When he wouldn't, she grew angry.
She told lies about him to Potiphar.
Potiphar gave Joseph no chance to explain
and threw him into prison.

"What will happen to me now?" sighed
Joseph.

But God was still taking care of him. Soon, the prison warder noticed how well Joseph behaved, and put him in charge of all the other prisoners. There were two special prisoners – Pharaoh's butler, and Pharaoh's baker. One night, they each had a dream.

Joseph told them what their dreams meant. Sadly, in three days' time, the baker would be killed. But in three days' time, the butler would be set free, and would work for Pharaoh again.

"When you see Pharaoh, please tell him I'm here, though I've done nothing wrong!" begged Joseph.

"Of course I will!" smiled the butler. But when Joseph's words came true, and the butler did go back to the palace, he forgot all about Joseph — until Pharaoh had a dream. And no one could tell him what it meant. Then the butler remembered Joseph. Pharaoh sent for him.

"I cannot tell you what the dreams mean," said Joseph, "but God will give me the answer." Joseph listened as Pharaoh told him about the dreams. Then Joseph said, "The seven fat cows mean seven years of good harvests. The seven thin cows mean seven years of famine will come afterwards."

"What?" cried Pharaoh in alarm.

Joseph said, "During the seven good years, the people must store corn in the barns. Then you will have food for the seven years of famine."

"Of course!" cried Pharaoh. And he put Joseph in charge of all Egypt, second only to himself, so that Joseph could see that the plan was carried out.

One day, Joseph's brothers came to Egypt to buy food. They didn't recognize him, and they *did* bow down to him. Joseph had forgiven them long ago. "I'm your brother!" he said. "Don't be afraid! You did wrong, but God brought good from it." Then Jacob also came to Egypt. And the family was very happy.

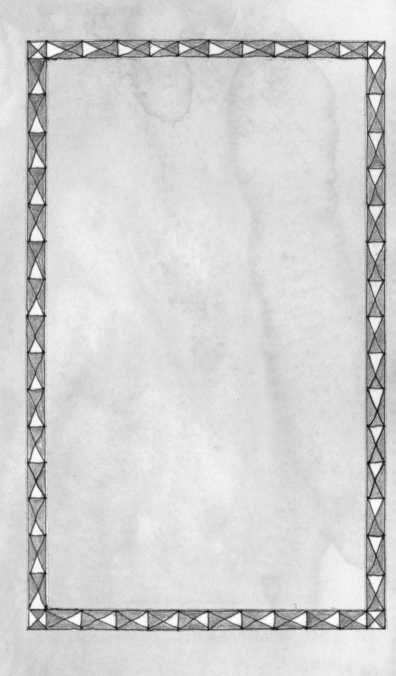